03/10

Please return on or before the latest date above.
You can renew online at www.kent.gov.uk/libs
or by phone 08458 247 200

CUSTOMER SERVICE EXCELLENCE

Libraries & Archives

Kent
County
Council

*You do not need to read this page –
just get on with the book!*

First published in 2008 in Great Britain by
Barrington Stoke Ltd
18 Walker Street, Edinburgh, EH3 7LP

www.barringtonstoke.co.uk

Reprinted 2009

ISBN: 978-1-84299-558-7

Printed in Great Britain by Bell & Bain Ltd

Scottish
Arts Council

Contents

Chapter 1
Crazy Gran

Ben's gran was crazy.

"Did I tell you about Tim?" she said.

"Yes," said Ben. "Lots of times."

His gran lived with Ben and his mum and dad. She told him about Tim over and over again.

"We went in a boat," Gran said. "Tim fell in. He went right under. He got all wet."

"I know," said Ben. "You told me."

Tim was Gran's brother. He was dead.
He fell in the sea and drowned, a long time
ago, when he was a child. Just Ben's age.

"Are you Tim?" Gran asked Ben.

"No," said Ben. "I'm Ben."

"But you fell in," said Gran.

"No," said Ben. "Tim fell in. Your brother."

"Tim, yes," Gran said. "You fell in."

Ben's dad came in.

Gran forgot about Ben. "Ah," said Gran. "*You're* Tim. We went in a boat. You fell in."

"Not me, love, I'm Fred," Dad said. "And I'm off on a job. Got to fix a shower. Want to come, Ben?"

"Yes, please," said Ben.

Dad was a plumber. He put in pipes and fixed baths and showers, and he put tiles on walls. Ben liked tiles. They made the job look so good.

"Shower," said Gran. "Water. My brother Tim –"

"I know," said Dad. "Fell in the water, didn't he?"

Ben's mum came in from the kitchen.

"Off you go," she said to Ben and Dad. "Go and fix your shower. Gran and I will be OK."

"Tim fell in," Gran said.

"We'll have a nice cup of tea," said Mum.

Chapter 2
On the Way

In the van, Ben asked, "Why is Gran so crazy? Tim died ages ago, when she was a child. He drowned. Can't she remember?"

"Her mind is in a muddle," said Dad.

"Why?" asked Ben. "Was her mind always in a muddle?"

8

"No," said Dad. "When I was a lad, she was great. She did the shopping and cooked the food and told us all what to do. But later on, like I said, she started to get muddled."

"Can't she get unmuddled?" asked Ben.

"No," said Dad. "She can't learn new things any more. She goes over and over the old ones."

"We have to learn things at school," said Ben. "It's boring. I don't want to learn things."

"Yes, you do," said Dad. "If you don't learn, you're in a mess like Gran."

"I'm not like Gran," said Ben. "She can't send a text. She can't even put the telly on."

"Telly," said his dad. "That's all you think about."

"No, it's not," said Ben. "I want to learn to put tiles on a wall, like you do."

"Tiles are great," said Dad. "They make a wall look good. But you need to learn about taps and pipes and tanks. And water flow. It's all part of a plumber's job."

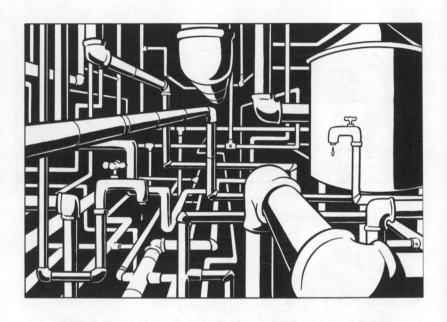

"What's water flow?" asked Ben.

"Water flow is the way water runs round the pipes," said Dad. "But it's a lot to learn."

"I can't learn to be a plumber at school," said Ben.

"Yes, you can," Dad said. "You can learn to read. You can learn maths. The more you do, the better you get. You can learn anything, if you try."

"Don't want to try," said Ben.

Dad got cross. "Yes, you do want to try," he said. "You don't get to be a plumber just by sitting around and thinking you like tiles – any fool can do that. You need to get off your bum and do some work."

"Oh, shut up," muttered Ben.

"Don't you tell me to shut up!" Dad shouted. "You kids these days think you know it all. You sit there, texting each other and stuffing your faces with crisps, never do a thing. I'm fed up with it."

Ben was fed up, too, but he didn't say any
more.

Chapter 3
Wet Dad

Dad stopped the van by a house and got out. He was still cross.

Ben looked at the house. "Is there anyone in?" he asked.

"No. Got to get the key from next door," said Dad. "Go and ask the woman – you can do that, can't you? Not too much work?" He

was still cross.

Ben went next door and rang the bell. A woman opened the door. She was wearing a long dress with daisies on, and big ear rings.

"Hello!" she said. "Are you the plumber?"

"My dad is," said Ben. "I've come to get the key."

She gave him the key. "The family don't come here much," she said. "They live in town. They were here last week, and said the shower had no water in it. So I told them to ring your dad."

"Yes," said Ben. "Thanks."

He went back to the house next door. His dad had got the tool-box out of the van. Ben gave him the key, and they went in. Ben

saw a note on the kitchen table. It said
PLUMBER, but Dad didn't look at it.

"There's a note," said Ben.

"Think I'm stupid?" said Dad. "I don't
need a note. I know where the shower room
is, they told me on the phone. It's next to
the toilet." He went to find it.

Ben went after him. Dad was looking at the shower.

"It's not the electric sort," said Ben.

"It works off the hot water tank," said Dad.

He turned the shower tap on. No water came out.

"Where is the hot water tank?" asked Ben.

"In the attic," said Dad.

"I'll get the ladder from the van," said Ben.

"You can't do it on your own," said Dad. He was not so cross now. He went out to the van, with Ben after him. They got the ladder off the top of the van and took it in the house, then dragged it up the stairs.

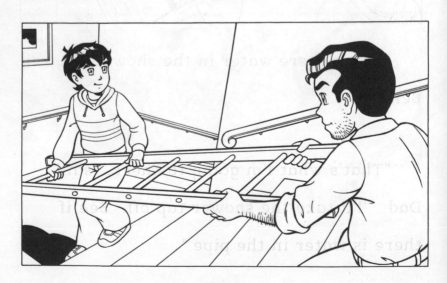

"I'll just check the water flow," said Dad.
They put the ladder up, and Ben held it
while Dad went up to the attic. Then he
came down and said, "There's water in the
tank OK."

"But is there water in the shower?" asked
Ben.

"That's what I'm going to check," said
Dad. "I'll take the shower tap off. See if
there is water in the pipe."

They went back to the shower room. Ben handed Dad a spanner, and he began to undo the tap.

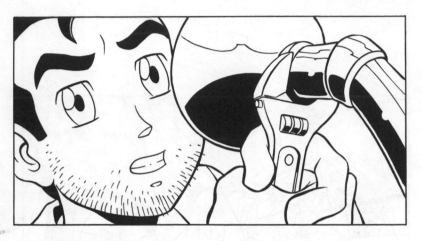

"Now this is a thing you can learn," he said. "How to undo a tap. There may be water in it, so you must go slowly. Turn it just a little way. Not too far. Just a little way, like this. Or it might –"

Water shot out. It blew the tap out of the pipe. The tap fell on Dad's foot.

"Ow!" shouted Dad and he hopped about on one leg.

The shower spray fell off and landed in the shower tray. Water shot out all over Dad. He jammed his hand over the pipe, but he could not stop the flow.

"Turn the water off!" he shouted. "Main tap."

"Where is the main tap?" asked Ben.

"I don't know. Go and look. Hurry up!"

Chapter 4
Water Flow

Ben ran up the ladder and looked in the attic. No main tap. He came down the ladder and ran to the bath-room. No main tap. He looked in at the door of the shower room. Dad was still standing in the shower tray but it was full of water. He had his hand over the pipe. But water was still

shooting out of the shower spray and Dad
was soaking wet. Water was pouring over
the edge of the shower tray all over the
floor.

"I said, *turn it off!*" Dad yelled.

"I'm looking for the tap," said Ben. He
wanted to say something about water flow,
but he didn't.

He ran into the kitchen. The note was
still on the table. Ben picked it up and
looked at it. There was a lot of writing on
it, but there was a bit at the bottom in big
letters. MAIN TAP IN KITCHEN, BY BACK
DOOR. LOW DOWN.

Ben smiled. If Dad had read the note, he'd know where the main tap was. Dad was yelling from the shower room, "Ben, hurry up! Water is getting everywhere!"

Ben bent down and turned the tap off. Then he went back to the shower room. The water had stopped, but the flood was running out into the hall. Dad was trying to mop it up with the bath mat.

"Get the mop from the van," he said. "And a bucket."

Ben ran out to the van. He got the mop and the bucket, and some old sheets, too. He

took them back to the shower room, and started mopping.

Dad took his boots off. They were full of water. He tipped the water down the loo, but his boots were soaked. His socks were soaked, too. His hair was soaked. He was soaked all over. Water dripped off him.

Ben said, "If I could drive, I would go home and get you some dry things."

"But you can't," said Dad.

"If you phoned Mum, she could bring some dry things," said Ben. "On the bus."

"She can't leave Gran," said Dad.

"Gran could come, too," said Ben. But he knew that was a silly idea.

Dad knew, too. "Don't even think of it," he said.

"Right," said Ben. It was hard to get Gran out of the house. It took ages to find her hand-bag and her hat and all the stuff she needed, and as soon as you got her into her coat she took it off again.

"I'll get another mop," Ben said. "There's one in the kitchen."

"Good," said Dad.

It took a long time to mop up all the water. All the old sheets from the van were soaked.

At last Dad said, "Right. Let's get the ladder on the van."

They took the ladder down the stairs and put it on the van. Then they put in all the wet sheets and the mop and bucket and the tool-box. Ben put the other mop back in the kitchen. Dad was still soaking wet. He put his wet boots back on.

"OK," he said. "Let's get out of here."

They went out. The woman from next door was standing by the van.

"You've had a flood," she said. "I saw you putting all that wet stuff in the van."

"Um – well – yes," said Dad.

"You can't go home like that," said the woman. "You're soaking wet. You'll get your death of cold. Come in, and I'll get you some dry clothes."

She led them into the house, and gave Dad a pair of leggings that looked too small and a green T-shirt with spots on, a pink fleece jacket and a pair of red socks.

"I can't wear that stuff!" said Dad.

"Yes, you can," said the woman. "Go and change in the bath-room. Hurry up!" She was very bossy, but Ben could see she was right. It was a cold day, and his dad might get ill if he drove home all wet.

Dad came out of the bath-room looking very funny. The leggings were much too short, and the spotty T-shirt and pink fleece made him look totally mad. Ben was falling about, but the woman didn't laugh. She was wearing things like that herself.

She gave Dad a black bin bag and said, "You can put your wet stuff in this."

"Thank you," said Dad.

Chapter 5
Who's Smiling Now?

The windows of the van kept misting over. Dad's hair was still wet, and so were his boots.

After a bit, Ben said, "I'm sorry I said, 'Shut up'."

"It's OK," said Dad. "I'm sorry, too.
I should have read the note."

They drove on for a bit, then Dad said,
"You know, I was like you at school. I didn't
bother with lessons. They were so boring.
So I never passed any exams. Getting to be
a plumber was really hard. It took me
ages."

Ben nodded. Then he said, "There's a lot to learn. Things like water flow."

"Water flow," said his dad. "Well, yes."

He ran his hand over his wet hair, and he and Ben both laughed.

When they got home, they went into the kitchen. "What have you got on?" asked Ben's mum.

"We had a flood," said Ben. "Dad was showing me how to undo a tap. A bit at a time."

"Shut up," said Dad.

"Sorry," said Ben. "But anyway, the woman next door gave him dry things."

"So I see," said Mum. And she started to laugh.

Gran came in. She said, "Did I tell you about Tim? We went in a boat –"

Then she looked at Dad.

"You are wearing funny clothes," she said, "And your hair is wet. You fell in the water. Are you Tim?"

"No I'm Fred," said Dad.

They were all laughing. Gran laughed, too.

"Silly Tim," she said. "You think I'm crazy. But I'm not. You fell in, I can see that. Your hair is all wet. And your boots."

Ben felt sorry for her. "Yes, he did get wet," he said.

Gran was still laughing, but it was a bit sad. Her brother Tim was dead. He drowned a long time ago, but Gran still loved him. She still kept thinking about him because she was in a muddle.

Ben gave Gran a hug.

"You're right," he said. "He got wet. My wet dad."

Barrington Stoke would like to thank all its readers for commenting on the manuscript before publication and in particular:

Tim Andrews

Bradley Bedden

Amelia Browne

Amy Buckland

Callum Day

Bailey Ford

Sarah Griffin

Louise Isaacs

Calum Kennedy

Peter King

Alex Langton

Rachel Langton

Paul Maddon

Sean McGil

Rebecca Metton

Tiago Silva

Kieron Skelton

Lea Smith

Jessye Yabro

Become a Consultant!

Would you like to give us feedback on our titles before they are published? Contact us at the email address below – we'd love to hear from you!

info@barringtonstoke.co.uk
www.barringtonstoke.co.uk

Ready for more? Try ...

Snow Dogs

by
Jane A. C. West

Zeb wants to win the dog sled race.
But will he die before he gets
to the end?

You can order *Snow Dogs* from our website at
www.barringtonstoke.co.uk

Ready for more? Try ...

United, Here I Come!

by
Alan Combes

Joey and Jimmy are very bad at football. But Jimmy is sure he will play for United one day. Is Jimmy crazy – or will he get there?

Ready for more? Try ...

Thin Ice

by
Chris Powling

Pete knows that you must not walk on ice. But a dog is stuck out there on the lake! Pete has to help ... what can he do?

You can order *Thin Ice* from our website at
www.barringtonstoke.co.uk